LITERATURE & WRITING

EXPLORING
HISTORICAL
FICTION

SCHOLASTIC INC.

PERMISSIONS— "Janette's Winter" by Barbara Bloom. Copyright © 1985 by Barbara Bloom. First published in Cricket, October 1985. "A Crown of Wild Olive" from Heather, Oak and Olive by Rosemary Sutcliff. Copyright © 1972 by Rosemary Stucliff. Reprinted by permission of Murray Pollinger. Chapters 1-2 from Timmy O'Dowd and the Big Ditch: A Story of the Glory Days on the Old Erie Canal by Len Hilts. Copyright © 1988 by Len Hilts. Reprinted by permission of Harcourt-Brace Jovanovich, Inc.

ISBN 0-590- 49300-0

CONTENTS

JANETTE'S WINTER

by
Barbara Bloom

Illustrated by
Chi Chung

T he sun was just beginning to set over the Montana mountains that September day in 1849. Its rays were still warm, yet Janette Riker shivered and drew her homespun shawl tighter around her shoulders. Eagerly, fearfully, she looked from one snowcapped peak to another. Except for the green grasses bending gently in the breeze, there was no movement.

"Oh, where *are* you?" she whispered anxiously. "Papa, why don't you and the boys come back? What's happened to you?"

Janette and her father and two brothers had stopped their Conestoga wagon in this lovely mountain valley to rest the oxen and hunt fresh game. They knew they couldn't stay long—the season was late, and they were in a hurry to reach Oregon. So yesterday, while Janette washed their clothes in the small gurgling stream, her father and the boys went hunting. They promised to bring home meat in time for dinner.

Late that afternoon Janette started a campfire, her mouth

watering for the taste of fresh, roasted meat. But evening came without any sign of the three men, and before long Janette was surrounded by the vast, dark silence. Fearing the wild animals she knew roamed the hills, she climbed into the wagon, snatched the rifle from its rack, and sat with her back pressed against the wooden backboard.

All night she crouched like that, listening for the return of her family, but she heard only the howling of wolves and the wailing of the night winds. When the sun first showed above the jagged mountains, she jumped from the wagon.

At first it was easy to follow the tracks left by her father and brothers the day before. But after a few miles the trail disappeared in the powdery sands of a dry riverbed. Janette ran along the banks in both directions crying, "Papa! Tom! Billy!"

At the foot of the mountains she shouted, but only her own voice echoed back from the overhanging rocks. Hour after hour she wandered among the hills around the valley, calling. But there was no answer.

In the late afternoon she returned to camp, finding nothing. Knowing nothing.

Now, standing utterly alone in the wilderness, she trembled with fear. Their two oxen were grazing peacefully nearby, and Janette threw her arms around one of them. "Surely they'll come back soon," she said. Then she set about preparing for another long, sleepless night in the wagon—alone.

The days that followed became a blur in Janette's memory. Every morning she set out in a new direction, calling and searching for her father and brothers. At night she returned, exhausted, to the empty meadow and the patient oxen. She grew accustomed to sleeping alone in the wagon, and even to the howling of the wolves, but her dreams were filled with visions of her father and brothers, lost and perhaps hurt somewhere in the wilderness around her. Once she thought she heard Tom's voice calling to her from the darkness, but it was only the wind sighing in the pine trees.

Finally one morning, Janette just stood and stared at the tall mountains rising all around her. She did not know where else to look for her family. Hours later, when the sun began to set, she forced herself to admit the horrible truth. Her father and brothers were not coming back. She was alone in the middle of a vast, fierce wilderness. Turning to the oxen she cried, "What's to become of me? I can't drive the wagon through those passes!"

Her only answer was the rustle of the wind in the trees and the contented munching of the animals.

It was too much for Janette. She sank to the ground and sobbed. Her wails and moans echoed through the valley, but she knew that no one could hear her. There would be no wagon along the trail until spring.

Janette cried until she could cry no more. Then at last she tried to shake off her grief. She drew a deep breath and smelled the sweet, fresh earth. She knew that she couldn't take the wagon over the mountains by herself and that she would have to stay in this valley until help came. But to survive the winter, she would need a shelter.

Janette got up and wiped her eyes. She went to the wagon, found the ax, and walked to the woods. There she began chopping down trees. She worked until her arms ached, but

by sundown she had felled only two birch saplings. The next day she cut down two more trees, and the day after, three.

Finally, after a week's hard work, she had fifteen saplings of about the same length. With the spade she dug holes side by side in the earth until they formed a small circle fifteen steps around. Into each hole Janette set a tree. Then she dragged the butter churn to the center of the circle and climbed up on it to lash the saplings together. When she finished, her shelter looked like a tepee. The next day she pulled up clumps of prairie grass and stuffed them between the cracks, so the wind could not get in. And she stretched the white canvas cover from the Conestoga wagon over her shelter, so the rain could not fall through the top. She hammered the canvas firmly into the ground with the stakes her father had brought to mark off their new land in Oregon. Janette left one flap open to use as a door.

"Look at that!" She proudly showed her oxen the odd little

shelter, which had taken her over two weeks to build. Her shoulders hurt, and she had blisters on her hands, but still she laughed.

Then she blinked hard to stop her tears, for no one was there to laugh with her.

After a while Janette pulled the half-empty bags of coffee, rice, sugar, salt, flour, beans, and corn meal down from the wagon and into her house. She pushed the small iron stove over the side of the wagon and dragged it in, too, along with all the wool blankets and buffalo robes. On top of the stack of blankets she gently laid the patchwork quilt her mother had sewn before she died. This would be her bed.

That night it rained, and in the morning there was frost on the ground. Once again Janette shouldered her ax and made for the forest, this time to chop the wood she would need to keep her stove burning throughout the winter.

The nights were growing colder and the hours of sunlight

fewer, and finally the day came when she had to break through the ice of the small stream so the oxen could drink. All day she thought of the animals. They were the only companions she had, and she loved their dear, familiar faces, but she would need their meat more than their company if she were to last the winter.

The next morning Janette took up the rifle and stood before the fatter ox. Trembling, she aimed at its broad forehead, closed her eyes, and pulled the trigger. The gun kicked her shoulder and knocked her onto the ground, but the huge beast fell dead.

Slowly Janette rose and brought out the butcher knife. She cut into the hind flesh and carved pieces larger than her hand. Each one she covered with salt and stacked in a barrel. Though she had never done it by herself before, she had watched her father pack away meat every fall since she was a small child.

That night Janette was awakened from an exhausted sleep by fierce, savage growls outside her hut. The noise sounded like mad dogs, but she knew it must be wolves or mountain lions, attracted by the smell of the freshly slaughtered meat. They paced around Janette's shelter, sniffing and clawing and scratching at the canvas. For a moment she could hardly breathe—what if they forced their way inside? Throwing off her quilt, Janette pushed several logs in front of the door flap and cocked her rifle.

"Don't come in," she prayed desperately. But the clawing and scratching became more violent, and Janette feared the worst—when suddenly she heard other noises farther away. A savage scream from an animal, galloping scrambles, commotion—then silence. Had they gone?

Janette relaxed her grip on the rifle. She began trembling

violently, but she could not hear any more noises. The night seemed endless.

The next morning she saw many animal tracks in the soft earth around her shelter, but her one remaining ox was gone. She never found out if the creature had sought refuge in the woods—or if it had been killed by the hungry wolves. The next night the wild animals returned, and the next, and the next throughout the long autumn. Every night Janette sat up with her rifle, afraid to sleep. Every morning she was stiff and tired.

Then, one afternoon, the snow began to fall. Janette brought in an extra supply of logs, and that night she heard the wind blowing wildly outside as she snuggled under her warm quilt. In the morning she couldn't crawl out of her hut, but she managed to cut a small hole in her canvas roof and dig away the snow to make a smoke hole for her stove. Shivering, she piled on fresh wood and waited out the storm.

When Janette finally tunneled her way outside two days later, snow lay deep in the valley, almost as high as her shelter. She caught her breath at the wild beauty of it all—and tried not to think how utterly alone she was.

Day after day Janette heard the howl of the wind as it drove the snows before it. Every morning she cleared the smoke hole in her roof and cooked beans and corn cakes. On clear days she trudged to the woods to chop more logs for her wood pile and kept a careful lookout for wild animals. But after the first heavy snowfall she was never again bothered by them.

Often during that long, cruel winter, Janette sat inside and thought of her family. She remembered the gentle sound of her father's voice, Tom's face with its broad smile, Billy's deep

laugh. More and more, she dreamed of the happy times they had spent together back home in Illinois. How she longed for the familiar white farmhouse with the blue flowers growing by the door— and the people she loved safe inside its walls!

As the slow days passed into weeks and the weeks into months, Janette grew pale and thin. Her food supply grew dangerously low, and she began rationing her already skimpy meals.

Then one day the call of an eagle pierced her quiet. Janette crawled outside in time to see the huge bird flying lazily across the sky. She felt a mild wind brush her cheeks and saw that the snow was melting from the pine branches. It must be spring! Janette's heart began to beat wildly. Perhaps now some other settlers would pass through her valley!

But the spring thaw brought new troubles for Janette. Within a week the warm sun had turned the snowdrifts into small, muddy rivers. Water covered the floor of her shelter, soaking her bed and flooding her stove.

Janette knew that she must leave her winter home. The wagon stood above the wet ground, its gray frame bare as a skeleton. Gathering the last of her strength, she pulled the shabby canvas from her shelter and draped it back over the wagon frame. She carried her mother's quilt, the rifle, the almost empty bag of corn meal, and the last few pieces of

salted meat back to the wagon bed.

All the rest of that day, Janette sat huddled in the wagon. With no way to build a fire, she ate her meat raw and her corn meal uncooked. At night she fell into an uneasy sleep, her dreams punctuated by the steady *drip, drip* of the melting snow. The days that followed turned into weeks as Janette, exhausted, kept her eyes on the distant mountain passes, hoping to see a wagon. She had done all she could to save herself. Now, with no fire and precious little food left, she simply waited—and hoped.

Then, one morning when patches of grass had begun appearing in the flooded valley, Janette heard hoofbeats. She shook with excitement but was too weak to climb out of the wagon. The sound of horses came nearer, and her trembling grew worse. At last she struggled to the end of the wagon and threw open the flap.

There, arranged in a semicircle around her, was a small band of Indian braves mounted on pinto ponies. Janette knew the Indians in these parts did not take kindly to white settlers invading their land, but her relief at seeing other human faces overcame whatever fear she might have felt.

"Please," she said, "help me. Papa—Tom—Billy—they've all gone."

The hunting party stared at her, impassive, as their ponies snorted and pawed the ground.

Then Janette lost all the self-control that had kept her alive throughout her ordeal. She didn't know whether the Indians could understand her language, but the words burst from her like the rushing waters of a spring stream. She told the Indians about arriving in the valley and losing her family. She told them about searching the surrounding mountains, about building her shelter and gathering fuel. She told them about killing her ox, about hearing the wolves, about eating raw meat and corn meal. But mostly she told them about living alone through the long, dark winter months.

As she spoke, the braves looked from Janette to her shelter, to the wagon, and back to Janette. She couldn't seem to stop talking. They must understand—they must!

Slowly, the Indian who appeared to be their leader nodded his head. "Brave," he said, gesturing to her makeshift camp. "Very brave."

Janette drew a deep breath. Whether he had understood her words or just seen for himself what she had gone through, he had understood! She brushed away tears as the Indian slid off his pony.

"Come," he commanded, holding out a hand to help her from the wagon. "We will go to your people."

"People," Janette whispered. And this time she didn't try to stop the flow of tears.

In that spring, more than one hundred years ago, the Indians took Janette Riker across the mountains to the white settlement that is now Walla Walla, Washington. There she stayed for a time, questioning all the travelers who stopped by on their way West. But no one ever found any sign of her father and brothers. Janette later married a pioneer and lived to a very old age. And her daughters and granddaughters and even their daughters never tired of telling the story of how she had survived the winter of 1849—alone.

A CROWN OF WILD OLIVE

from

Heather, Oak and Olive

by

Rosemary Sutcliff

Illustrated by

Ken Joudrey

At the Olympic Games, Amyntas and Leon became friends. During the training period, Leon accidentally cuts his foot. Amyntas finds himself hoping that perhaps Leon, his strongest competitor, will not be able to run the race. He purchases a small statue of a bull with silver horns. Amyntas offers the bull to Zeus, saying: "…Let me keep a clean heart in this, let me run the best race that is in me, and think of nothing more."

I t was still early in the day, but already it was growing hot; the white dry heat of the Greek summer; and the faint off-shore wind that made it bearable had begun to feather the water, breaking and blurring the reflections of the galleys lying at anchor in Pireaus Harbour.

Half of Athens, it seemed, had crowded down to the port to watch the *Paralos*, the State Galley, sail for the Isthmus, taking their finest athletes on the first stage of their journey to Olympia.

17

EXPLORING HISTORICAL FICTION

Every fourth summer it happened; every fourth summer for more than three hundred years. Nothing was allowed to stand in the way, earthquake or pestilence or even war—even the long and weary war which, after a while of uneasy peace, had broken out again last year between Athens and Sparta.

Back in the spring the Herald had come, proclaiming the Truce of the Games; safe conduct through all lands and across all seas, both for the athletes and for those who went to watch them compete. And now, from every Greek state and from colonies and settlements all round the Mediterranean, the athletes would be gathering...

Aboard the *Paralos* was all the ordered bustle of departure, ropes being cast off, rowers in their places at the oars. The Athenian athletes and their trainers with them had gathered on the afterdeck. Amyntas, son of Ariston, had drawn a little apart from the rest. He was the youngest there, still several months from his eighteenth birthday and somewhat conscious that he had not yet sacrificed his boy's long hair to Apollo, while the rest, even of those entered for the boys' events— you counted as a boy at Olympia until you were twenty—were already short-haired and doing their Military Service. A few of them even had scars gained in border clashes with the Spartans, to prove that their real place, whatever it might be on the race track or in the wrestling pit, was with the men. Amyntas envied them. He was proud that he had been picked so young to run for Athens in the Boys' Double Stade, the Four Hundred Yards. But he was lonely. He was bound in with all the others by their shared training; but they were bound together by something else, by another kind of life, other loyalties and shared experiences and private jokes, from which he was still shut out...

That night they beached the *Paralos* and made camp on the easternmost point of the long island of Salamis; and not long past noon next day they went ashore at the Isthmus and took horse for Corinth on the far side, where a second galley was waiting to take them down the coast. At evening on the fifth day they rode down into the shallow valley where Olympian Zeus, the Father of Gods and men, had his sanctuary, and where the Sacred Games were celebrated in his honour.

What with the long journey and the strangeness of everything, Amyntas took in very little of that first evening. They were met and greeted by the Council of the Games, whose president made them a speech of welcome, after which the Chief Herald read them the rules. And afterwards they ate the

evening meal in the athletes' mess; food that seemed to have no more taste nor substance than the food one eats in a dream. Then the dream blended away into a dark nothingness of sleep that took Amyntas almost before he had lain down on the narrow stretcher bed in the athletes' lodging, which would be his for the next month.

He woke to the first dappled fingers of sunlight shafting in through the doorway of his cell. They wavered and danced a little, as though broken by the shadows of tree branches. Somewhere further down the valley a cuckoo was calling, and the world was real again, and his, and new as though it had been born that morning. He rolled over, and lay for a few moments, his hands behind his head, looking up at the bare rafters; then shot off the bed and through the doorway in one swallow-dive of movement, to sluice his head and shoulders in the icy water trickling from the mouth of a stone bull into a basin just outside. He came up for air, spluttering and shaking the water out of his eyes. For a moment he saw a colonnaded court and the plane tree arching over the basin through a splintered brightness of flying droplets. And then suddenly, in the brightness, there stood a boy of about his own age, who must have come out of the lodging close behind him. A boy with a lean angular body, and a dark, bony face under a shock of hair like the crest of an ill-groomed pony. For a long moment they stood.looking at each other. Then Amyntas moved aside to let the other come to the conduit.

As the stranger ducked his head and shoulders under the falling water, Amyntas saw his back. From shoulder to flank it was criss-crossed with scars, past the purple stage but not yet

faded to the silvery white that they would be in a few years'
time; pinkish scars that looked as though the skin was still
drawn uncomfortably tight over them.

He must have made some betraying sound or movement,
because the other boy ducked out from under the water,
thrusting the wet russet hair back out of his eyes, and
demanded curtly, "Have you never seen a Spartan back before?"

So that was it. Amyntas, like everyone else, had heard dark
stories of Spartan boys flogged, sometimes to death, in a ritual
test of courage, before the shrine of Artemis Orthia, the Lady
of the Beasts.

"No," he said, "I am Athenian." And did not add that he
hoped to see plenty of Spartan backs when once he had started
his military service. It was odd, the cheap jibe came neatly
into his head, and yet he did not even want to speak it. It was
as though here at Olympia, the Truce of the Games was not
just a rule of conduct, but something in one's heart. Instead,
he added, "And my name is Amyntas."

They seemed to stand confronting each other for a long
time. The Spartan boy had the look of a dog sniffing at a
stranger's fist and taking his own time to make sure whether it
was friendly. Then he smiled; a slow, rather grave smile, but
unexpectedly warm. "And mine is Leon."

"And you're a runner." Amyntas was taking in his build and
the way he stood.

"I am entered for the Double Stade."

"Then we race against each other."

Leon said in the same curt tone, "May we both run a good race."

"And meanwhile—when did you arrive, Leon?"

"Last night, the same as you..."

And then it was the first day of the Festival; the day of solemn dedication, when each competitor must go before the Council to be looked over and identified, and take the Oath of the Games before the great bronze statue of Zeus of the Thunderbolts.

The day passed. And next morning before it was light, Amyntas woke to hear the unmistakable, unforgettable voice of the crowds gathering in the Stadium. A shapeless surf of sound, pricked by the sharper cries of the jugglers and acrobats, and the sellers of water and honeycakes, myrtle and victors' ribbons calling their wares.

This was the day of the Sacred Procession; the Priests and Officials, the beasts garlanded for sacrifice, the athletes marching into the waiting Stadium, while the Herald proclaimed the name and state of each one as he passed the rostrum. Amyntas, marching in with the Athenians, heard his own name called, and Leon's, among names from Samos and Cyrene, Crete and Corinth and Argos and Megara. And he smelled the incense on the morning air, and felt for the first time, under his swelling pride in being Athenian, the thread of his own Greekness interwoven with the Greekness of all those others. This must have been, a little, the thing their Great Grandfathers had felt when they stood together, shield to shield, to hurl back the whole strength of invading Persia, so that they might remain free. That had been in a Games year, too...

The rest of that day was given over to the chariot and horse races; and that night Amyntas went to his sleeping cell with the thunder of hooves and wheels still sounding somewhere behind his ears. He seemed to hear it in his dreams all night, but when he woke in the morning, it had turned into the sound that he had woken to yesterday, the surf-sound of the gathering crowd. But this morning it had a new note for him, for this was the Day, and the crowd that was gathering out there round the Stadium was his crowd, and his belly tightened and the skin prickled at the back of his neck as he heard it.

He lay for a few moments, listening, then got up and went out to the conduit. Leon came out after him as he had done that first morning of all, and they sluiced down as best they could. The water barely dribbled from the mouth of the stone bull now, for—with the vast gathering of people, and the usual end-of-summer drought, the water shortage was getting desperate, as it always did by the time the Festival days arrived.

"How is the foot?" Amyntas asked.

"I can't remember where the cut was, unless I look for it."

They stood looking at each other, the friendship that they had never put into words trying to find some way to reach across from one to the other.

"We cannot even wish each other luck," Amyntas said at last, helplessly.

And Leon said, almost exactly as he had said it at their first meeting, "May both of us run a good race."

They reached out and touched hands quickly and went their separate ways.

The next time they saw each other, they were waiting for the track, with the rest of the Double Stade boys just outside the arched way into the Stadium. The Dolichus, the long distance

race, and the Stade had been run, each with its boys' race immediately after. Now the trumpet was sounding to start the Double Stade. Amyntas' eyes went to meet Leon's, and found the Spartan boy's slightly frowning gaze waiting for him. He heard the sudden roar of the crowd, and his belly lifted and tightened. A little stir ran through the waiting boys; the next time the starting trumpet sounded, the next time the crowd gave that roar, it would be for them. Hippias was murmuring last-minute advice into Amyntas' ear, but he did not hear a word of it... He was going out there before all those thousands upon thousands of staring eyes and yelling mouths, and he was going to fail. Not just fail to win the race, but *fail*. His belly was churning now, his heart banging away right up in his throat so that it almost choked him. His mouth was dry and the palms of his

hands were wet; and the beginnings of panic were whimpering up in him. He looked again at Leon, and saw him run the tip of his tongue over his lips as though they were suddenly dry. It was the first time he had ever known the Spartan boy to betray anything of what was going on inside him; and the sight gave him a sense of companionship that somehow steadied him. He began to take deep quiet breaths, as he had been taught, and the rising panic quietened and sank away.

The voice of the crowd was rising, rising to a great roar; the Men's Double Stade was over. He heard the Herald crying the name of the winner, and another roar from the crowd; and then the runners were coming out through the arched entrance; and the boys pressed back to let them past, filthy with sweat and sand and oil. Amyntas looked at the face of the man with the victor's ribbons knotted round his head and arms, and saw that it was grey and spent and oddly peaceful.

"Now it's us!" someone said; and the boys were sprinting down the covered way, out into the open sundrenched space of the Stadium.

The turf banks on either side of the broad track, and the lower slopes of the Kronon Hill that looked down upon it were packed with a vast multitude of onlookers. Half-way down on the right-hand side, raised above the tawny grass on which everybody else sat, were the benches for the Council, looking across to the white marble seat opposite, where the Priestess of Demeter, the only woman allowed at the Games, sat as still as though she herself were carved from marble, among all the jostling, swaying, noisy throng. Men were raking over the silver sand on the track. The trumpeter stood ready.

They had taken their places now behind the long white limestone curbs of the starting line. The Umpire. was calling: "Runners! Feet to the lines!"

Amyntas felt the scorching heat of the limestone as he braced the ball of his right foot into the shaped groove. All the panic of a while back had left him. He felt light, and clear headed, and master of himself. He had drawn the sixth place, with Leon on his left and the boy from Megara on his right. Before him the track stretched white in the sunlight, an infinity of emptiness and distance.

The starting trumpet yelped; and the line of runners sprang forward like a wave of hunting dogs slipped from the leash.

Amyntas was running smoothly and without hurry. Let the green front-runners push on ahead. In this heat they would have burned themselves out before they reached the turning post. He and Leon were running neck and neck with the red-headed Macedonian. The Rhodian had gone ahead now after the front-runners, the rest were still bunched. Then the Corinthian made a sprint and passed the boy from Rhodes, but fell back almost at once. The white track was reeling back underfoot, the turning post racing towards them. The bunch had thinned out, the front-runners beginning to drop back already; and as they came up towards the turning post, first the boy from Macedon, and then Nikomedes catching fire at last, slid into the lead, with Amyntas and Leon close behind them. Rounding the post, Amyntas skidded on the loose sand and Leon went ahead; and it was then, seeing the lean scarred back ahead of him, that Amyntas lengthened his stride, knowing that the time had come to run. They were a quarter of the way down the home lap when they passed Nikomedes; the Megaran boy had taken fire too late. They were beginning to overhaul the redhead; and Amyntas knew in his bursting heart that unless something unexpected happened, the race must be between himself and Leon. Spartan and Macedonian were going neck and neck now; the position held for a few paces, and then the redhead gradually fell behind. Amyntas was going all out, there was pain in his breast and belly and in the backs of his legs, and he did not know where his next breath was coming from; but still the thin scarred back was just ahead. The crowd were beginning to give tongue, seeing the two come through to the front; a solid roar of sound that would go on rising now until they passed the finishing post. And then suddenly Amyntas knew that something was wrong;

Leon was labouring a little, beginning to lose the first keen edge of his speed. Snatching a glance downward, he saw a fleck of crimson in the sand. The cut had re-opened.

His body went on running, but for a sort of splinter of time his head seemed quite apart from the rest of him, and filled with an unmanageable swirl of thoughts and feelings. Leon might have passed the top of his speed anyway, it might be nothing to do with his foot—But the cut *had* re-opened... To lose the race because of a cut foot... It would be so easy not to make that final desperate effort that his whole body was crying out against. Then Leon would keep his lead...

And at the same time another part of himself was remembering his father standing on the quayside at Piraeus as the *Paralos* drew away—crying out that he was not running only for himself but for Athens, his City and his people... A crown of wild olive would be the greatest thing that anyone could give to his friend... It would be to insult Leon to let him win... you could not do that to your friend... And then, like a clean cold sword of light cutting through the swirling tangle of his thoughts, came the knowledge that greater than any of these things were the Gods. These were the Sacred Games, not some mere struggle between boys in the gymnasium.

He drove himself forward in one last agonizing burst of speed, he was breathing against knives, and the roar of the blood in his ears drowned the roar of the crowd. He was level with Leon—and then there was nothing ahead of him but the winning post.

The onlookers had crowded right down towards it; even above the howl of the blood in his head he heard them now, roar on solid roar of sound, shouting him in to victory. And then Hippias had caught him as he plunged past the post; and he was bending over the trainer's arm, bending over the pain in his belly, snatching at his breath and trying not to be sick. People were throwing sprigs of myrtle, he felt them flicking and falling on his head and shoulders. The sickness eased a little and his head was clearing; he began to hear friendly voices congratulating him; and Eudorus came shouldering through the crowd with a coloured ribbon to tie round his head. But when he looked round for Leon, the Spartan boy had been swept away by his trainer. And a queer desolation rose in Amyntas and robbed his moment of its glory.

Afterwards in the changing room, some of the other boys came up to congratulate him. Leon did not come; but when they had cleaned off the sand and oil and sweat, and sluiced down with the little water that was allowed them, Amyntas hung about, sitting on the well kerb outside while the trainer finished seeing to his friend's foot. And when Leon came out at last, he came straight across to the well, as though they had arranged to meet there. His face was an unreadable as usual.

"You will have cooled off enough by now, do you want to drink?" Amyntas said, mainly because somebody had to say something; and dipped the bronze cup that always stood on the well kerb in the pail that he had drawn.

Leon took the cup from him and drank, and sat down on the well kerb beside him. As Amyntas dipped the cup again and bent his head to drink in his turn, the ends of the victor's ribbon fell forward against his cheek , and he pulled it off impatiently, and dropped it beside the well.

"Why did you do that?" Leon said.

"I shall never be sure whether I won that race."

"The judges are not often mistaken and I never heard yet of folk tying victors' ribbons on the wrong man."

Amyntas flicked a thumb at Leon's bandaged foot. "You know well enough what I mean. I'll never be sure whether I'd have come first past the post, if that hadn't opened up again."

Leon looked at him a moment in silence, then flung up his head and laughed. "Do you really think that could make any difference? It would take more than a cut foot to slow me up, Athenian!—You ran the better race, that's all."

It was said on such a harsh, bragging note that in the first moment Amyntas felt as though he had been struck in the face. Then he wondered if it was the overwhelming Spartan pride giving tongue, or simply Leon, hurt and angry and speaking the truth. Either way, he was too tired to be angry back again. And which ever it was, it seemed that Leon had shaken it off already. The noon break was over, and the trumpets were sounding for the Pentathlon.

"Up!" Leon said, when Amyntas did not move at once. "Are you going to let it be said that your own event is the only one that interests you?"

They went, quickly and together, while the trainer's eye was off them, for Leon was under orders to keep off his foot. And the people cheered them both when they appeared in the Stadium. They seldom cared much for a good loser, but Leon had come in a close second, and they had seen the blood in the sand.

The next day the heavyweight events were held; and then it was the last day of all, the Crowning Day. Ever after, Amyntas remembered that day as a quietness after great stress and turmoil. It was not, in truth, much less noisy than the days that had gone before. The roaring of the Stadium crowds were gone; but in the town of tents the crowds milled to and fro. The jugglers with knives and the eaters of fire shouted for an audience and the merchants cried their wares; and within the Sacred Enclosure where the winners received their crowns and made their sacrifices before the Temples of Zeus and Hera, there were the flutes and the songs in praise of the victors, and the deep-voiced invocations to the Gods.

But in Amyntas himself, there was the quiet. He remembered the Herald crying his name, and the light springy coolness of the wild olive crown as it was pressed down on his head; and later, the spitting light of pine torches under

the plane trees, where the officials and athletes were feasting. And he remembered most, looking up out of the torchlight, and seeing, high and remote above it all, the winged tripods on the roof of the great Temple, outlined against the light of a moon two days past the full...

Next morning in all the hustle of departure, he and Leon contrived to meet and slip off for a little on their own.

The whole valley of Olympia was a chaos of tents and booths being taken down, merchants as well as athletes and onlookers making ready for the road. But the Sacred Enclosure itself was quiet, and the gates stood open. They went through, into the shade of the olive trees before the Temple of Zeus...

They stood among the twisted trunks and low hanging branches, and looked at each other and did not know what to say. Already they were remembering that there was war between Athens and Sparta, that the Truce of the Games would last them back to their own states, but no further; and the longer the silence lasted, the more they remembered.

From beyond the quiet of the Enclosure came all the sounds of the great concourse breaking up; voices calling, the stamping of impatient horses. "By this time tomorrow everyone will be gone," Amyntas said at last. "It will be just as it was before we came, for another four years."

"The Corinthians are off already."

"Catching the cool of the morning for those fine chariot horses," Amyntas said, and thought, There's so little time, why do we have to waste it like this?

"One of the charioteers had that hunting knife with the silver inlay. The one you took a fancy to. Why didn't you buy it after all?"

"I spent the money on something else." For a moment Amyntas was afraid that Leon would ask what. But the other boy only nodded and let it go.

He wished suddenly that he could give Leon something, but there was nothing among his few belongings that would make sense in the Spartan's world. It was a world so far off from his own. Too far to reach out, too far to call. Already they seemed to be drifting away from each other, drifting back to a month ago, before they had even met. He put out a hand quickly, as though to hold the other boy back for one more moment, and Leon's hand came to meet it.

"It has been good. All this month it has been good,' Leon said.

"It has been good," Amyntas agreed. He wanted to say, "Until the next Games, then." But manhood and military service were only a few months away for both of them; if they did meet at another Games, there would be the faces of dead comrades, Spartan or Athenian, between them; and like enough, for one of them or both, there might be no other Games. Far more likely, if they ever saw each other again, it would be over the tops of their shields.

He had noticed before how, despite their different worlds, he and Leon sometimes thought the same thing at the same time, and answered each other as though the thought had been spoken. Leon said in his abrupt, deadlevel voice, "The Gods be with you, Amyntas, and grant that we never meet again."

They put their arms round each other's necks and strained fiercely close for a moment, hard cheekbone against hard cheekbone.

"The Gods be with you, Leon."

And then Eudorus was calling, "Amyntas! Amyntas! We're all waiting!"

And Amyntas turned and ran—out through the gateway of the Sacred Enclosure, towards where the Athenian party were ready to start, and Eudorus was already coming back to look for him.

As they rode up from the Valley of Olympia and took the tracks towards the coast, Amyntas did not look back. The horses' legs brushed the dry dust-grey scrub beside the track, and loosed the hot aromatic scents of wild lavender and camomile and lentisk upon the air. A yellow butterfly hovered past, and watching it out of sight, it came to him suddenly, that he and Leon had exchanged gifts of a sort, after all. It was hard to give them a name, but they were real enough. And the outward and visible sign of his gift to Leon was in the little bronze bull with the silvered horns that he had left on the Offering Table before the feet of Olympian Zeus. And Leon's gift to him... That had been made with the Spartan's boast that it would take more than a cut foot to slow him up. He had thought at the time that it was either the harsh Spartan pride, or the truth spoken in anger. But he understood now, quite suddenly, that it had been Leon giving up his own private and inward claim to the olive crown, so that he, Amyntas, might believe that he had rightfully won it. Amyntas knew that he would never be sure of that, never in all his life. But it made no difference to the gift.

The track had begun to run downhill, and the pale dust-cloud was rising behind them. He knew that if he looked back now, there would be nothing to see.

TIMMY O'DOWD AND THE BIG DITCH

by
Len Hilts

Illustrated by
John Gampert

When Timmy heard the brassy blare of Cap'n Sam's horn, he dropped his shovel and dashed from the stable to the wharf. Although the *Glory Be* was still a mile up the canal, he could see Cap'n Sam standing in all his splendor on her bridge, looking ten feet tall in his top hat. The bright blue of his frock coat matched the azure of the sky, and the horn at his lips glinted like a jewel in the sunlight.

Timmy's heart raced. Not another packet on the canal could hold a candle to the *Glory Be*. While Cap'n Sam strutted, passengers lounged on the forward deck and on top of the cabin, chatting and sipping cool drinks.

For a moment, Timmy saw himself standing by the tiller,

master of all he could see—the proud *Glory Be*, the canal before him, the passengers, the horses. He felt wonderful.

Someday, someday . . .

Billy, the hoggee riding the second horse in the boat's two-horse hitch, moved the team smartly along the towpath. The strong gait of the matched black horses kept the towrope taut. When asked, they could haul the packet at eight miles an hour—even though that was well over the speed limit.

Timmy smiled. Cap'n Sam demanded a smart, fast traveling pair for his boat every time he switched teams at his line's replacement stables.

Grandfather heard the horn, too, and hurried from the bunkhouse, limping to favor his game leg. He'd been playing checkers with the hurry-up crew. When he sat for a long time, his game leg took a while to warm up.

"Sounds like old Sam Blunt acomin'," he said. "No doubt he's speedin'. He allus does. Patrick ought to slap a fine on him."

"He's trying to break the Schenectady-to-Buffalo record," Timmy said.

"He's been tryin' for ten years," Grandfather scoffed. He squinted for a better look, then shook his head. "He's a sight, that old Blunt, dressed like a rooster struttin' on the hen-yard fence. Look at that! Yellow pantaloons, no less!"

Timmy grinned in open admiration. "Someday that'll be me. I'll have a packet like that and a tall beaver hat like Cap'n Sam's. But I think I'll wear a bright red coat."

Grandfather snorted. "Not while I'm alive, you won't! Red coats are a sad sight for any Irishman."

TIMMY O'DOWD AND THE BIG DITCH

Timmy's mother joined them on the wharf.

"Timothy'll have himself a lovely emerald green coat, Michael. I'll see to it myself."

Her face was flushed from the heat of the kitchen. She untied her apron, threw it over her arm, and began poking strands of red hair into her bun. "I'm a sight," she said to no one in particular.

Grandfather chuckled. "You're a sight for these old eyes, Kate. I'll take you the way you are. If there's anythin' I like better'n you, it's your cookin'."

Kate blushed. "Away with you, Michael O'Dowd. I don't know which has more blarney in him, you or your son. You're both scoundrels." She looked around. "Where's your father, Timmy?"

"Da and Mr. Connarty took the boat to fix a leak at Weber's place," Timmy said. "He won't be long."

The hooves of the tow team sounded like the beating of a bass drum as they trotted from the towpath onto O'Dowd's wooden wharf.

Billy, the hoggee, grinned down at Timmy. "Hello, Irish. Say, have we got a surprise fer you on the boat!"

As he spoke, Cap'n Sam bellowed, "Whoa them down, Billy! We're pullin' in here for a minute." He leaned on the tiller, and the bow of the packet thumped the wharf.

The passengers turned toward the captain to see why they were stopping.

"This here is O'Dowd's place," Cap'n Sam announced in his ringmaster voice. "We're lettin' off a passenger." He paused, then shouted at Timmy's mother, "Kate! You bakin' today?"

She nodded.

Cap'n Sam roared, "Any of you got a taste for pie? Kate O'Dowd's are the best in all New York State!"

Kate muttered to Timmy, "I didn't bake that many."

But it was too late. The passengers were stepping to the wharf and heading her way. She fled to the kitchen.

Timmy watched Ethan, Cap'n Sam's black cabin boy, haul a heavy carpetbag and a heavier flat canvas case over the side. Behind him, a boy emerged from the cabin and disembarked. Timmy's eyes popped.

The boy, about his own age, wore a tailored suit and a wide-brimmed straw hat garnished with a bright yellow ribbon. His fine white linen shirt, topped by a tall, stiff collar, sported ruffles and a soft flowing neckerchief. To finish it off, he wore white stockings and shiny black shoes.

A real macaroni!

The boy stood beside his luggage and took in the wharf, the cobblestone house, the porch, the stables, and the bunkhouse. His face screwed into a frown that said he didn't want to be here.

Grandfather, staring, too, said, "That boy-o is surely dressed for a weddin' or a funeral. Nobody here is dead or gettin' married, so why's he gettin' off?"

Cap'n Sam swaggered from the boat and approached them with an envelope in his hand.

"Got a letter for you, Mr. O'Dowd," he said as he handed it to Grandfather, "from your son Donal in New York." He jerked his head toward the wharf. "That's his boy."

"Saints be!" Grandfather said. "You mean that's little Dennis?" His surprise turned to concern. "Has somethin'

TIMMY O'DOWD AND THE BIG DITCH

happened to Donal?"

Cap'n Sam laughed. "Naw, he's fine. Talked to him myself when he brought the lad to the dock at Schenectady."

He lowered his voice to a conspiratorial whisper. "He thinks the boy's too citified. Wants him to spend two weeks with Timmy so he can get to know his cousin and the canal."

The picture came together for Timmy. This was Dennis O'Dowd, the son of Uncle Donal, who lived in New York City. Uncle Donal used to work on the canal, but he went to the city with only a wagon and a team of horses. Soon he had a dozen teams working for him, what with all the hauling business because of canal freight. Kate read his infrequent letters aloud to Grandfather.

"Your son's gittin' to be a rich man," Cap'n Sam said.

Grandfather eyed Dennis's fine clothes. "I can see that," he said.

Timmy sauntered over to Dennis. "I'm Timmy," he said. "We're cousins."

Dennis's eyes traveled from the top of Timmy's tattered straw hat to his dusty bare feet. His upper lip curled a little, and his nose twitched.

"Do you always dress like that?" he asked.

"'Cept when I go to church," Timmy replied. "This is how everybody dresses around here. We work."

Now Timmy slowly walked around Dennis, playing the same game. He inspected the suit, the clean white shirt, the yellow ribbon on his cousin's hat. In all his days, he had never seen anyone dressed like that on a weekday. On Sunday maybe, but never on a weekday.

Dennis followed him with his eyes.

Timmy's curiosity itched. He had never touched a soft, smooth fabric like that of Dennis's jacket. He reached out to it.

Dennis jumped away. "Don't do that! It's velvet, and you'll get it dirty."

Timmy rammed his hands into his pants pockets.

"Well, you're a regular *dandy*, aren't you? Cap'n Sam says you're goin' to stay two weeks. You figure to dress like that the whole time?" Timmy chuckled as he pictured Dennis in his fancy clothes shoveling out the stable. Caring for the horses that pulled the hurry-up boat was one of Timmy's jobs. He had to see that the horses were fit to run hard when a canal wall breached, which meant hauling hay and water and shoveling a lot of manure. The crew had to reach the breaks quickly, before the water flooded the crops on nearby farms.

He said, "You goin' to work while you're here? A little manure might help the look of that velvet."

"I'm going to sketch," Dennis said defiantly.

"Sketch?" Timmy said. "What's that?"

"It means to draw."

"You goin' to draw pictures? I used to draw pictures when I was little. Not any more, though. Now I work."

Dennis had had enough of this conversation. He headed back toward the boat and said to Cap'n Sam, "I want to get back aboard. I'm not staying here."

Cap'n Sam had raised his horn, which hung on a gold chain around his neck, to his lips. He blew a long, resonant note, then announced in a booming voice, "All aboard now! The *Glory Be* is shovin' off!"

The passengers, standing around a table on the porch, finished off their slices of succulent peach pie. Kate was giving them damp cloths to wipe the sweet juice from their fingers before they hurried back to the boat.

Timmy watched Michael O'Dowd approach the newcomer. "Dennis," he said, "I'm your grandfather. Shake hands."

Dennis took the old man's hand respectfully. "Good afternoon, sir."

Grandfather said, "Well, now, it's a fine thing to have you visitin' me for a while. We'll have some talks, you and me and Timmy."

Dennis looked sheepish. "I'm sorry, Grandfather, but I'm not staying," he said. "I can't stay."

"No?" Grandfather said. "And why would that be?"

"Well," Dennis said uncertainly, "I don't think I have the right clothes."

"Aw now, Dennis." Grandfather laughed. "Do you think we've got no extra clothes at all around here? Sure, just as soon as you take off that fine suit, Timmy'll give you some sturdy workin' clothes. You'll have no problems."

Cap'n Sam gave another blast on the horn and reached out to shake Grandfather's hand. "I'll pick the boy up in two weeks, Mr. O'Dowd," he said.

"But I'm not staying!" Dennis protested.

Grandfather put his arm around Dennis and steered him toward his baggage.

"Now just get your bags there, Dennis, and we'll go inside. I'll introduce you to the leprechaun that lives with us. Timmy'll show you the stables and the horses. Come along now, boy."

"Leprechaun?" Dennis looked up at his grandfather, startled. "He lives with you?"

"Grandfather!" Timmy protested, "Don't tell him that. No leprechaun lives with us."

"Well," said Grandfather with twinkling eyes, "he doesn't exactly *live* with us. But he's around all the time just the same, makin' one mischief after another. I don't doubt he's over there in the weeds right now, watchin' us every minute."

Kate came from the kitchen. "If that fool leprechaun is watching us," she said sharply, "why don't you have him carry the boy's bags, Michael?"

TIMMY O'DOWD AND THE BIG DITCH

She turned, all smiles, to Dennis. "Welcome to our house, Dennis O'Dowd. It's glad I am to have you here. And how are your father and mother? We haven't seen them in a month of Sundays."

Timmy's insides curdled. His mother was trying to make the little stuffed shirt feel welcome. He shook his head. This was going to be a long two weeks.

Dennis picked up his bag. Kate said, "Timmy, give him a hand."

Timmy had to use both hands to swing the canvas case up to his shoulders. *It must be loaded with rocks*, he thought. *What in the world can the little dandy have in it?*

Struggling under the weight, he followed his mother and his cousin to the house. His eyes fell on Dennis's jacket. He felt a strong urge to wipe his sweaty palms on the beautiful fabric.

Grandfather chuckled softly. "Your face looks like a prune."

"Am I *really* goin' to have him around for weeks, Daideo?" Timmy asked desperately.

Grandfather's hand was warm on his shoulder. "Let me lean on you, boy-o, while we walk. Me leg is achin' a bit."

They started up the path. "Timmy," the old man's voice came soft, "Dennis is an O'Dowd, one of us. He's got to have a lot of good in him, even if it's hard to see under them clothes. But when he tastes life here on the canal, the good will come out. See if it don't."

Cap'n Sam gave one final blast on his horn as the boat moved out into the canal. Then he shouted, "Timmy, I nearly forgot. You goin' to be my apprentice on the *Glory Be* next summer?"

The misery inside Timmy skyrocketed into elation. He spun

around so fast he almost knocked Grandfather down.

"You bet, Cap'n Sam! You bet I will!"

Billy flicked his whip over the horses, and the *Glory Be* pulled away toward Buffalo.

Grandfather looked after the boat and shook his head. "Does your father know about this?" he asked...

Kate and Dennis were already inside. Timmy followed, blinking in the subdued light after the bright sun. He dropped the canvas case with a loud thud and said, "Here are your rocks."

"Those are my books," his cousin told him. "You don't have

TIMMY O'DOWD AND THE BIG DITCH

to wreck them, do you?"

"Books!" Timmy blurted. "Jehoshaphat! What for?"

Dennis shrugged and turned back to Kate. She was in the middle of the big room, saying, "This is where we do most of our living in this house, Dennis, the keeping room."

Dennis put his bag down and surveyed the room. A stone fireplace half filled one wall. To the right of the fireplace was a wooden sink and a black wood-burning stove. A big table with a dozen chairs stood a short distance from the stove.

"That side's my kitchen, " she said. "We eat at the table."

"It's a big table for just four people."

"Oh, there's more than four of us," Kate said. "Did you see the bunkhouse next door? The six men of the hurry-up crew sleep there and eat with us in here."

She pointed to the other side of the room, where chairs were arranged in a comfortable semicircle. "That's our sitting room," she said.

She indicated two doorways in the back wall, hung with bright flowered curtains. "That room is Grandfather's and the other is where Mr. O'Dowd and I sleep."

"Where's Timmy's room?"

Kate pointed to a ladder. "Up in the loft. There's plenty of room up there for both of you."

Exasperation clawed at Timmy. There it was already! Dennis was to wear his clothes, sleep in his loft. Well, the dandy could carry his own heavy baggage up the ladder.

Kate said, "Timmy will stuff a straw ticking for you."

Timmy thought, *no dumb city dandy would know how to do that, so I have to do it for him*. He started to protest, but Grandfather's fingers squeezed his shoulder in warning. His voice was low. "Dennis is our guest."

When loud voices sounded outside, Timmy shouted, "Da's back," and ran out to the wharf.

Patrick O'Dowd was watching the hurry-up crew run the boat into its slip, cut into the canal wall. With the boat in, he dropped the wooden wharf extension in place.

"Kate, we're home," he shouted. "When's supper?"

Kate appeared on the porch with Dennis at her side.

O'Dowd turned to Timmy, "Who's that?"

Timmy made a face. "Cousin Dennis from New York City."

"Donal's boy?" O'Dowd's face brightened with delight. "Is Donal here, too?"

"Just him," Timmy said, jerking his thumb in the direction of the house.

O'Dowd darted an amused look at his son.

"Don't like him much, do you?"

Timmy stared at the ground and shook his head.

"What'd he do to you?"

Timmy couldn't explain why he didn't like Dennis. The boy hadn't done anything. It was just—well, that he was there. But that wouldn't make any sense to his father.

"Aw, I guess it's his clothes and all," he said finally.

O'Dowd welcomed Dennis with a cheery, "'Pon my soul, lad, you're the very image of your father. How is Donal, and your mother?"

Dennis flushed and shook hands. "Just fine, sir. They said to give you their best."

Kate murmured, "What nice manners!"

TIMMY O'DOWD AND THE BIG DITCH

Timmy glowered. Nobody ever said *his* manners were nice. They just told him to mind them.

"Kate," O'Dowd said, "if we've a few minutes before supper, I'll show Dennis the hurry-up boat."

"Ten minutes," Kate told him and went inside.

"Come on, Dennis." O'Dowd put his arm around the velvet jacket. "I'll bet you've never seen a hurry-up boat in the city."

The two started toward the wharf. Timmy trotted after them, frowning.

On the deck of the hurry-up boat, O'Dowd told Dennis, "When the canal was dug, the dirt from the channel was piled up to make the walls on either side."

From where Dennis stood, the canal looked like two long earthen embankments with water between them.

"How deep is the water?" he asked.

"Four feet," his uncle replied. "But now they've started makin' it deeper so bigger boats can use the canal. It's forty feet wide at the top and twenty-eight feet at the bottom. The sides are tapered."

Dennis leaned over the water to study the tapering walls. "The captain of the *Glory Be* told us how the walls sometimes break. They look pretty solid to me."

"Oh, that they are," O'Dowd said, "except when they're abused. High waves from speedin' canal boats lap at them. And when heavy rains overfill the canal, the walls get soft and mushy."

"Why didn't they make the walls of stone?" asked Dennis. "The locks are stone. Why not the walls?"

"Good question," O'Dowd said. "The canawlers built locks

49

and aqueducts of stone, but stone construction was too slow and costly for the whole 363 miles. You see, a lot of New Yorkers thought the canal was a bad idea. They called it Clinton's Ditch, and grumbled at every dollar Governor Clinton spent. So Clinton and the canawlers tried to finish the Erie as soon as possible, to prove what a grand idea it was."

"How long did it take?"

"Seven years," O'Dowd told him.

"Did everyone like the canal after that?"

"Most everyone. And why not? The canal makes money for the state, and it's turned New York City into the country's biggest port.

"The most amazin' thing," he continued, "is that the first canawlers didn't know anything about canal buildin'. They were mostly farmers, but they used their native good sense, made the walls of dirt, and got the job done.

"Critics were bettin' the dirt banks wouldn't hold the water. The day they let water into the canal, most everyone held his breath, just waitin' for the walls to collapse. But they worked fine. The canawlers had fooled 'em by linin' the walls with clay."

"But they do break open," Dennis reminded him.

"True, and we have to watch 'em careful-like. But with the canal makin' money, we're rebuildin' it a bit at a time. It's goin' to be wider and deeper, and it's goin' to have stone walls. Meanwhile, we've got to make those dirt banks hold."

He turned back to the hurry-up boat. "Anyway, when the walls break open, the water pours onto farms next to the canal—and all tarnation busts loose. You've never seen anyone

madder than a farmer when his land is flooded. Believe me, we pay dearly in damages."

"How many hurry-up boats are there?" Dennis asked.

"Oh, one every thirty miles or so along the canal. We run like rabbits to fix breaks before too much water gets out."

He laughed. "I tell you, Dennis, next to a wet farmer, the maddest man in the world is a barge captain whose boat is grounded because the water level has dropped."

Dennis's eyes traveled over the materials and equipment neatly stacked on the deck.

"Do you use all of this?" he asked.

"We keep most everything we need to fix a bad break." He pointed to a pile of boards. "Like those planks. We ram them into breaches in the berm. They stop the water flow while we patch the hole."

"Berm?"

"Oh, that's what canawlers call the canal walls: berms. The towpath is on the top of the berm on this side."

They walked forward on the boat.

"We use that hay," he said, indicating golden bales of hay in the bow, "for smaller breaks. We make patches with mud, sticks, and hay."

Neat coils of rope lay near the cabin. Inside, dozens of tools—spades, picks, shovels, pry bars, axes, and big wooden mallets—hung on racks. A row of lanterns stood on a shelf near the window. "We can even work at night if we have to," O'Dowd said.

Timmy, perched on a rope coil, watched his father's performance. *You'd think he was showin' the boat to President Polk himself*, he thought. *Maybe we ought to have a brass band.*

The noisy clatter of an old cowbell shattered the late afternoon quiet. Grandfather, swinging the bell on the porch, shouted, "Supper's ready!"

Timmy jumped down, relieved that the hurry-up boat tour was over.

"Come on, Da. Time to eat."

Dennis's place at the table was between Timmy and Grandfather. He stood behind his chair while the others noisily pulled out theirs and settled at the table. The leathery faced men of the crew sat around the lower end of the table.

Grandfather said, "Aren't you goin' to sit, Dennis?"

The boy glanced at Kate, who was carrying serving dishes from the big wood stove to the table. She smiled broadly. "It's all right, Dennis. Don't wait for me. I thank you for the courtesy, but we don't stand on ceremony here."

Dennis sat down, and his uncle said grace.

Timmy's appetite was sharp and ready. Dinner, their big meal, was at noon, but by suppertime Timmy was always hungry again.

Tonight they had one of his favorites—sliced beef to lay on Kate's brown-crusted bread and drown with her good brown gravy.

The clinking of knives and forks was the only sound in the room as everyone got down to business. When Dennis took only a small helping of beef and one piece of bread, Timmy nudged him.

"Better take all you want right now," he advised.

Grandfather laughed. "He's right, Dennis. If a platter gets past you, it may never come back." He nodded at the crewmen. "Those vultures eat like every meal was their last."

Sean Connarty, the crew chief, who was nearly as old as Grandfather, guffawed. "Don't let the old man tease you, boy. Nobody ever left Kate O'Dowd's table hungry."

Grandfather turned to Dennis. "Eatin' is pretty important to us, Dennis. When we were lads in Ireland, we were lucky to get a few potatoes for supper."

Connarty nodded. "When we came to America, things were so bad we didn't even have *potatoes*. It's even worse over there now."

Dennis looked at his grandfather. "My father said you came from Ireland to work on the canal."

"Aye," Grandfather said. "'Twas in 1817. You see, the canal people sent Mr. Canvass White to England to study the canals there. Before he came back, he hired a famous Irish canal man, J. J. McShane, to come over here to help. Old McShane told him he needed some strong Irish backs to get the job done. So we were hired."

"Aye," Connarty said . "Strong backs and weak minds!"

"Now, Sean, the work was hard, but you know it was lovely to have it—and the good things we got from it."

"Good things and bad," Connarty agreed. "Don't forget the mosquitoes big as horses, the cholera and swamp fever. Do you mind the time we worked the Montezuma Swamp, near Rochester, Michael? It's a wonder we ever finished that part, with every man down sick most of the time."

"We never would have, except by workin' in the winter," Grandfather replied, "when the skeeters took their holiday."

After everyone had eaten, Kate brought in the peach pie. "Only one piece each tonight," she said sternly. "That fool Blunt sold all the rest to his passengers. He's always doing that. I wish he'd warn me in advance."

"Now, Kate," her husband said, laughing, "you know you like the extra money. How else could you buy the material for pretty dresses like the one you're wearin'?"

Kate shook her head. "That won't work, Patrick O'Dowd. Your blarney gets you only one piece of pie, like everyone else."

The crewmen laughed.

While waiting for his pie, Grandfather pushed back his chair and walked to the door. He peered out for a moment, then returned.

"The leprechaun has his umbrella out," he announced.

The crew burst into laughter, and Connarty turned to Dennis. "That means the old man's corns are hurtin' and it's goin' to rain. He allus blames it on the leprechaun."

"My corns *are* achin' somewhat," Grandfather admitted. "But when that little green fella gets his bumbershoot out, you can wager it's goin' to be a bad un. He don't like to get wet."

Connarty pushed back from the table. "Well, boys, it's bed for us. We could be up and runnin' afore mornin'."

EXPLORING HISTORICAL FICTION

This book was set in Novarese
and composed by Marjorie Campolongo
It was printed on 50 lb. Finch Opaque.
Title page illustration by Ken Joudrey

Editor: Deborah Jerome-Cohen
Design: Patricia Isaza